THERE WAS AN OLD LADY WHO SWALLOWED A MOOSE

Chrissy Bozik

illustrated by Scot Ritchie

Scholastic Canada Ltd.
Toronto New York London Auckland
Sydney Mexico City New Delhi
Hong Kong Buenos Aires

Scholastic Canada Ltd.
604 King Street West, Toronto, Ontario M5V 1E1, Canada

Scholastic Inc.
557 Broadway, New York, NY 10012, USA

Scholastic Australia Pty Limited
PO Box 579, Gosford, NSW 2250, Australia

Scholastic New Zealand Limited
Private Bag 94407, Botany, Manukau 2163, New Zealand

Scholastic Children's Books
Euston House, 24 Eversholt Street, London NW1 1DB, UK

www.scholastic.ca

The art for this book was created using pencil and ink.
This was scanned into the computer where all the colouring was done

Library and Archives Canada Cataloguing in Publication

Title: There was an old lady who swallowed a moose / Chrissy Bozik ; illustrated by
Scot Ritchie.
Names: Bozik, Chrissy, author. | Ritchie, Scot, illustrator.
Identifiers: Canadiana 20190045205 | ISBN 9781443170420 (softcover)
Subjects: LCGFT: Stories in rhyme.
Classification: LCC PS8603.O9983 T54 2019 | DDC jC813/.6—dc23

6 5 4 3 2 1   Printed in Malaysia 108   19 20 21 22 23

For the whole team at Scholastic Canada,
with love!

— C. B.

To Steve and Elaine Collier,
for all the laughs we've shared.

— S. R.

There was an old lady who swallowed a moose.
What's the use in swallowing a moose?
It won't come loose!

There was an old lady who swallowed a lake
that gurgled and burbled and kept her awake.
She swallowed the lake to wash out the moose.
What's the use in swallowing a moose?
It won't come loose!

There was an old lady who swallowed some sticks.
What a trick to swallow a stick!
She swallowed the sticks to dam up the lake
that gurgled and burbled and kept her awake.
She swallowed the lake to wash out the moose.
What's the use in swallowing a moose?
It won't come loose!

There was an old lady who swallowed a beaver.
You wouldn't believe her, downing that beaver!

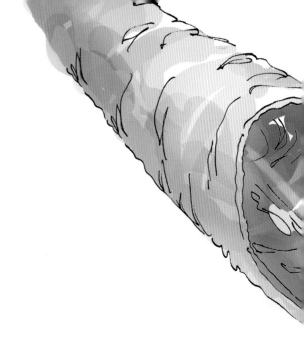

She swallowed the beaver to gnaw on the sticks.
She swallowed the sticks to dam up the lake
that gurgled and burbled and kept her awake.
She swallowed the lake to wash out the moose.
What's the use in swallowing a moose?
It won't come loose!

There was an old lady who swallowed a tent.
She really meant to swallow a tent!

She swallowed the tent to trap the beaver.
She swallowed the beaver to gnaw on the sticks.
She swallowed the sticks to dam up the lake
that gurgled and burbled and kept her awake.
She swallowed the lake to wash out the moose.
What's the use in swallowing a moose?
It won't come loose!

There was an old lady who swallowed a canoe.
What a thing to do, swallowing a canoe!
She swallowed the canoe to carry the tent.
She swallowed the tent to trap the beaver.
She swallowed the beaver to gnaw on the sticks.
She swallowed the sticks to dam up the lake
that gurgled and burbled and kept her awake.
She swallowed the lake to wash out the moose.
What's the use in swallowing a moose?
It won't come loose!

There was an old lady who swallowed a snake.
It was a mistake to swallow a snake!

She swallowed the snake to guide the canoe.
She swallowed the canoe to carry the tent.
She swallowed the tent to trap the beaver.
She swallowed the beaver to gnaw on the sticks.
She swallowed the sticks to dam up the lake
that gurgled and burbled and kept her awake.
She swallowed the lake to wash out the moose.
What's the use in swallowing a moose?
It won't come loose!

There was an old lady who swallowed a fire.
Who would desire to swallow a fire?
She swallowed the fire to scare the snake.
She swallowed the snake to guide the canoe.
She swallowed the canoe to carry the tent.
She swallowed the tent to trap the beaver.
She swallowed the beaver to gnaw on the sticks.
She swallowed the sticks to dam up the lake
that gurgled and burbled and kept her awake.
She swallowed the lake to wash out the moose.
What's the use in swallowing a moose?
It won't come loose!

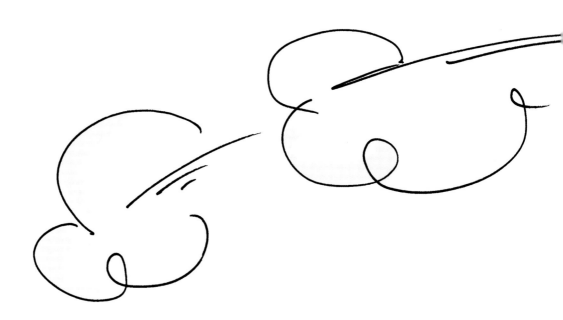

There was an old lady who swallowed the woods.
It did her no good, swallowing the woods!

She swallowed the woods to fuel the fire.
She swallowed the fire to scare the snake.
She swallowed the snake to guide the canoe.
She swallowed the canoe to carry the tent.
She swallowed the tent to trap the beaver.
She swallowed the beaver to gnaw on the sticks.
She swallowed the sticks to dam up the lake
that gurgled and burbled and kept her awake.
She swallowed the lake to wash out the moose.
What's the use in swallowing a moose?
It won't come loose!

Then that old lady, she swallowed a mosquito.
It itched, you know, to swallow a mosquito!
That mosquito buzzed and scratched and tickled!
The old lady squirmed and twitched and wiggled!
Then the old lady sneezed with all her might,
and out flew a great Canadian campsite!